COVERED BRIDGES of MADISON COUNTY IOWA

A Guide

Andrew R. Howard

photographs by the author

Third Printing

Other books by the author

Covered Bridges of Massachusetts - a Guide
Covered Bridges of Connecticut - a Guide
Covered Bridges of Bennington County
Vermont - a Guide
Covered Bridges of Virginia - a Guide

The Village Press
P. O. Box 174
Unionville, Connecticut 06085-0174

To Andy and Kathy

PREFACE

Madison County was chartered in 1846 and named for our fourth President, James Madison.

All of Madison County covered bridges are listed on the National Register of Historic Places.

The County, called the "Covered Bridge County of Iowa" is also made known by Robert James Waller's novel *The Bridges of Madison County* and the movie starring Meryl Streep and Clint Eastwood.

Originally claiming 19 covered bridges, the County had only seven by 1983. On October 8th of that year, the McBride Bridge was arsoned. The person responsible for the crime was placed on three years probation, required to reimburse the County $4,000 and perform 150 hours of community service.

Unfortunately, few records were kept about the bridges. As the years progressed, older residents died and their recollections were not recorded.

The Madison County Antique Association, founded in 1949, subsequently turned its attention to covered bridges. Working with the County Supervisors, they saw that the bridges were maintained and that they were named. The Association became closely associated with the bridges. When one was damaged by a truck passing through, the then President of the Association was called out of bed at night by an irate citizen and told to "do something about it."

In the late 1960's, the President of the Chamber of Commerce and three members of its Board came up with the idea of using the covered bridges as a means of promoting tourism in the County. The Madison County Covered Bridge Festival was born. Money was borrowed and also donated by the Chamber. A medallion was minted to commemorate each festival. Over the years the Festival grew and by 1979 its committee was basically independent, although still under the Chamber's wing. Each year, since 1971, a Senior Citizen King and Queen are chosen to preside over the festivities. A local brochure states that nearly 30,000 visitors attend the Festival each year - the second full weekend in October.

Photographs of each bridge detailing the portal and side views, as well as the truss design, are included in this guide. Also provided are the World Guide Number, type and length of truss, year built, the number of spans, and the stream that the bridge crosses.

Private covered bridges are not included in this guide.

ACKNOWLEDGEMENTS

I am indebted to The National Society for the Preservation of Covered Bridges, Inc. for permission to use their numbering system, which appears in the Society's publication: WORLD GUIDE TO COVERED BRIDGES.

Assistance from the following is gratefully acknowledged: Madison County Chamber of Commerce; Winterset Library; Winterset Museum; State Historical Society of Iowa; and the friendly and helpful people of Winterset.

I also wish to acknowledge, with many thanks, the use of information from the Madison County Historical Society's book: *Scenic Madison County , Iowa - Historical Significance,* compiled by Lloyd H. Smith, and the November 10, 1970 issue of *The Palimpset,* publication of The State Historical Society of Iowa.

A special "thank you" to my wife, Muriel, and my sister, Dorothea Howard, for their valuable suggestions and critical reading of the manuscript.

I wish to express my gratitude to Alfred D. Bauer for his patience and continued help in preparing the manuscript for publication.

CONTENTS

The Truss

Bridges

Bridge Builders

Eli Cox was born in Clinton County, Ohio in 1825. In 1846 he married Mary Mills, and was disowned from the church since his wife was not a Quaker. They had twelve children. Eli was a farmer, stock-raiser and a contractor who built a number of bridges, barns, and a schoolhouse. In 1868 he became Madison County's Supervisor. Two years later, he contracted his first covered bridge; the Cutler-Donahue Bridge.

Some of the work done on the bridges was by local farmers, working to pay their pole taxes, as was the custom in those days.

Little is known about H.P. Jones and G.K. Foster.

Why Were Bridges Covered?

Through the years many theories have been advanced as to why bridges were covered. One speculation was that the covering prevented horses from becoming frightened when crossing. Another notion was that animals would be misled into thinking they were entering a barn, and therefore would feel more at home. Others thought that the roof was meant to keep man, beast and a load of hay dry during a sudden storm. However, there is only one reason why bridges were covered: to protect truss members from the elements. It is a well known fact that wood will rot rather quickly if exposed alternately to moisture and sun.

Kissing Bridges

Undoubtedly, one of the side effects of covering a bridge was to encourage the timid suitor to steal a kiss from his date as their horse and buggy passed through. Perhaps, the longer the bridge the better! Many couples would carve their initials on the timbers or siding of the structure. This custom is still followed today together, unfortunately, with some undesirable material.

Wood Used

The timber used in the early bridges was generally white pine and southern pine simply because they were readily available. Both grow tall and straight. In old growth areas (where the forest has been untouched for many years), the trees are closely spaced and relatively free of low branches, thus producing clear timber with correspondingly more desirable properties.

Southern pine is structurally very desirable, with white pine somewhat less so, but easily worked with hand tools - an important factor in those days.

A tree consists of both heartwood and sapwood, the former having much resistance to decay, while the latter offers little resistance. In virgin or old growth forests, most species consist of a great deal of heartwood and very little sapwood, making the wood very desirable for bridge building.

Tree-nails (Trunnels) were of oak, generally two inches in diameter. It was a practice to soak them in oil.

Photographing Bridges

When is the best time of year to photograph a bridge? Actually this depends somewhat on the photographer's preference. The author's favorite season is the spring of the year just as buds are starting to blossom. Although some very charming photographs are taken of the bridges during the summer, a problem is sometimes presented by the surrounding trees and foliage obscuring part of the structure. If winter activities are enjoyed, there are possibilities for striking photographs to be taken from unusual vantage points such as the middle of a river, frozen or not, a snowmobile, or perhaps even on skis.

What camera should be used? The range can be from "aim and shoot" to an expensive 35 mm. camera, depending upon one's depth of interest in photography. Good pictures can be obtained from all of today's cameras.

Since most bridges have siding, there is a great brightness range between the dark inside and the brightly lit outside of the span. This range is so great that neither black and white nor color film can adequately record it. To avoid this problem, one may photograph the exterior and interior separately on either film. A shot of the exterior showing the shape and possibly the texture of the span, and an interior view capturing the detail of the bridge truss will then be in your possession. On some bridges a compromise can be reached by waiting until the sun is in such a position as to light part of the interior, before taking a shot on either film.

When arriving at a bridge, survey it and the surrounding area to determine the best angle and the time of day for a photograph. When shooting color, or for that matter black and white, do not hesitate to take a photograph in the early morning or late in the day. Some dramatic results can often be achieved. Take a number of pictures since film is very inexpensive considering the other items of the trip.

Good Luck!

TYPES OF TRUSSES

INTRODUCTION

Covered bridges have been built with many different trusses, but in Madison County, one type of truss dominates. It is the Town (or Towne) truss, named for its designer, Ithiel Town. The County bridges were built of northern white pine, and construction costs ranged from $900 to $1900.

The experience of walking through a covered bridge and observing the craftsmanship of the builders is further enriched by a little knowledge of the type of construction.

A triangle is the only polygon (a closed figure formed by straight lines in a plane) the shape of which cannot be varied without changing the length of one or more of its sides. This figure, also called a truss, is what gives the bridge its rigidity.

KINGPOST AND MULTI-KINGPOST TRUSS

The Kingpost Truss, which is probably the oldest truss, consists of two right triangles (A right triangle is one having a 90-degree angle.) placed so that these angles are back to back. The resulting vertical member is called the Kingpost, and is in tension when a load is placed on the bridge. In other words, this member tends to stretch. The horizontal member is called the lower chord and is also in tension under a load. The other members, which are on an angle, are in compression.

The Multi-Kingpost Truss is the result of combining a number of basic triangular Kingpost Trusses. There are many variations of this type. For example: It may contain an open center panel, an X center panel, or no center panel. Iron rods may also be used.

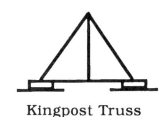

Kingpost Truss

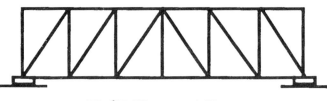

Multi-Kingpost Truss

16

QUEENPOST TRUSS

This was developed from the Kingpost Truss. The vertex of the latter is cut off parallel with the lower chord. A horizontal crosspiece is put in place, closing the figure. At both intersections where the crosspieces and the slanting pieces meet, a vertical member extending to the lower chord, is added. The horizontal crosspiece must not be connected to the top chord of the bridge. It is generally located immediately beneath it. Additional bracing may be used.

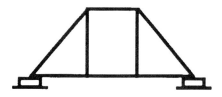

TOWN TRUSS

It is generally agreed that Ithiel Town (or Towne) (1784-1844) patented an original design (Jan. 28, 1820) for a bridge truss which bears his name. It consists of a series of planks crossed at approximately 90 degrees to each other and pinned together at each crossover with tree-nails (trunnels), resulting in a lattice. This was then placed at a 45-degree angle with the top and bottom chords.

The advantage of his design, among others, was that it proved inexpensive and easy to construct by local carpenters. He sold rights to his patent for one dollar per foot, and was one of the first successful bridge designers who could live off his royalties.The best information available indicates that he never built a bridge.

A carpenter in his youth and an architectural student, he is recognized for building the Center Church and Trinity Church on the Green at New Haven, Connecticut.

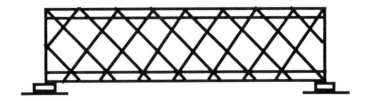

BRIDGES

Cutler-Donahue Bridge

Bridge 1   Truss: Town
WG: 15-61-02   Length: 83 ft.
Year Built: 1871   Spans: 1
                  Stream: Over a Gully

How to Get There: From the Madison County Chamber of
Commerce, in Winterset, travel one block south on John
Wayne Street (Rt. 169) and take a left onto South 9th Street.
Drive into the Winterset City Park where you will find ample
parking space on the right.

This was one of the first bridges built by Eli Cox. This bridge
and the Imes Bridge are the only ones that have a pitched roof.
The other spans have flat roofs, peculiar to this section of the
country. Originally spanning the North River some 18 miles
northeast of Winterset, the structure was moved to its present
site in 1970. The man in charge of moving the bridge was Clair
Rogers. His grandfather entered Madison County about the
time that the bridge was built. The structure, secured to a
house moving rig, was pulled by a 1934 truck. The procession
moved at the rate of one-half to twelve miles per hour,
depending on the terrain.

The bridge received a new roof and some replacement side
boards in 1997.

The afternoon provides a good time to take a photograph.

Bridge 1 Cutler- Donahue Bridge - Side View

22

Bridge 1 Cutler-Donahue Bridge - Portal View

Bridge 1 Cutler-Donahue Bridge - Truss View

Holliwell Bridge

Bridge 2
WG: 15-61-05
Year Built: 1880

Truss: Town & Arch
Length: 123 ft.
Spans: 1

Stream: Middle River

How to Get There: After visiting the Cutler-Donahue Bridge, return on 9th Street and take a right onto Court Street. Shortly you will see a sign to Imes and Holliwell Bridges. Drive to a "T" and take a right. The bridge may be seen 1 mile ahead, and 0.1 miles on the left.

The bridge was constructed by H.P. Jones and G.K. Foster.

In the early days the structure was part of a main highway spanning the river.

In 1995, the bridge was renovated at an approximate cost of $225,000.

The morning offers the best time for a photograph.

Bridge 2. Holliwell Bridge - Side View

Bridge 2 Holliwell Bridge - Portal View

Bridge 2 Holliwell Bridge - Truss View

Imes Bridge

Bridge 3
WG: 15-61-06
Year Built: 1871

Truss: Town
Length: 84 ft.
Spans: 1

Stream: Brook

How to Get There: After visiting the Holliwell Bridge, leave the park, and continue, shortly bearing right at a "Y". Drive 2 miles to a "T", and take a left. Drive 7 miles to the bridge, on the left.

The builder is unknown.

In January, 1870, it was voted to build a bridge at Wilkin's Ford, on the Middle River. Construction was to start as soon as the Brown Bridge (now no longer in existence) was completed and sufficient funds were available. The Imes Bridge was completed in June 1871, and known at that time as the Munger or Mills Bridge.

In 1887, it was moved to the Imes crossing of Clanton Creek, southwest of Hanley. The structure then became known as the Imes Bridge. In 1977, it was moved to its present location in eastern St.Charles.

In 1997, the bridge received a new roof.

The afternoon is a good time for a photograph.

Bridge 3 Imes Bridge - Side View

30

Bridge 3 Imes Bridge - Portal View

31

Bridge 3 Imes Bridge - Truss View

Cedar Bridge

Bridge 4	Truss: Town & Queenpost
WG: 15-61-03	Length: 77 ft.
Year Built: 1883	Spans: 1

Stream: Cedar Creek

How To Get There: From the Madison County Chamber of Commerce, drive one block south and take a left at the light. Drive to 10th street and take a left. The bridge will be 3 miles ahead on the left.

H.P. Jones, the builder, built the Cedar Bridge (also known as the Casper or Storrs Bridge) after he completed the Roseman Bridge.

The structure was moved to its present location in 1920 due to changes in Rt. 169.

Presently, this is the only bridge that is open to vehicular traffic. In 1998, the structure is scheduled for renovation at an estimated cost of $100,000.

There is a pleasant picnic area adjacent to the bridge.

The bridge is best photographed in the morning.

Bridge 4 Cedar Bridge - Side View

Bridge 4 Cedar Bridge - Portal View

Bridge 4 Cedar Bridge -Truss View

Hogback Bridge

Bridge 5   Truss: Town
WG: 15-61-04   Length: 108 ft.
Year Built: 1884   Spans: 1
Stream: North River

How To Get There: From the Madison County Chamber of Commerce, travel North on Rt. 169 for 2 miles and take a left. Drive another 2 miles and make a right. Continue for an additional 2 miles to the bridge on the left.

This bridge was also built by H.P. Jones. A board containing the names of all of the workers was placed in the bridge.

In 1992, the bridge was renovated at a cost of $118,810.

The afternoon provides a good time for a photograph.

Bridge 5 Hogback Bridge - Side View

Bridge 5 Hogback Bridge - Portal View

Bridge 5 Hogback Bridge - Truss View

Roseman Bridge

Bridge 6
WG: 15-61-07
Year Built: 1883

Truss: Town & Queenpost
Length: 106 ft.
Spans: 1

Stream: Middle River

How To Get There: Travel South from the Madison County Chamber of Commerce, and in 0.1 miles bear right. Continue 1 mile to a four-way stop, and pick up Rt. 92 West. Travel 4 miles and take a left. Drive 3 miles and take a left at the "T". Drive 1 mile and make a right, driving 0.1 miles to another "T". Take a right, and the bridge can be seen ahead.

The bridge was authorized in 1877, but not constructed until 1883. It was built by H.P. Jones.

The bridge in its picturesque setting was brought into prominence in the movie, *The Bridges of Madison County*, starring Meryl Streep and Clint Eastwood.

In 1992, the structure was renovated for the sum of $152,515.

The morning provides a good time for a photograph.

Bridge 6 Roseman Bridge - Side View

Bridge 6 Roseman Bridge -Portal View

43

Bridge 6 Roseman Bridge - Truss View

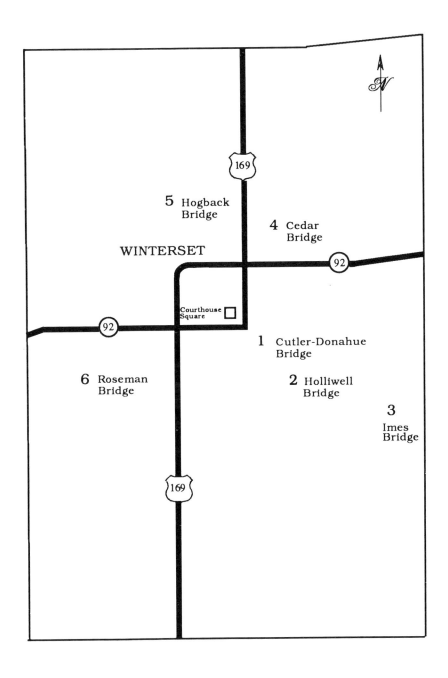

Map of Madison County Covered Bridges

COVERED BRIDGE SOCIETIES

Indiana C. B. Society, Inc.
725 Sanders Street
Indianapolis, IN 46203

Madison County Covered Bridge
    Preservation Association
P.O. Box 152
Winterset, IA 50273

National Society for the Preservation of
    Covered Bridges, Inc.
44 Cleveland Avenue
Worcester, MA 01603-1405

New York State C. B. Society
958 Grove Street
Elmira, NY 14901

Northern Ohio C. B. Society
938 Clearmount Ave., S.E.
North Canton, OH 44720

Southern Ohio C. B. Association
3155 Whitehead Road
Columbus, OH 43204

The C. B. Society of Oregon
9070 S.W. Rambler Lane
Portland, OR 97223

Theodore Burr C.B. Society
    of Pennsylvania, Inc.
P.O. Box 2383
Lancaster, PA 17603-2383

Zumbrota C.B. Society
7124 River Shore Lane
Champlin, MN 55316

Societe Quebecoise Des Ponts
    Couverts, Inc.
C. P. 102
St. Eustache, Qc J7R4K5
Canada

Notes